G000061016

Compiled by Geoffrey Marshall-Taylor
Arrangements by Douglas Coombes

BBC BOOKS

3

This anthology is a sequel to the 72 songs in *Come and Praise 1*. For this reason the numbering of items in this book begins at 73.

All the music in Come and Praise has been arranged by Douglas Coombes. These arrangements, which include melodic parts, guitar chords and simplified harmonies, may not be reproduced without due permission and acknowledgement.

The copyright holders of melodies and words are given below. Acknowledgement is due to the following whose permission is needed for multiple reproduction:

73: Music (c) 1987 Peter Rose. Words (c) 1987 Anne Conlon. Commissioned for BBC Songs of Praise by WWFUK; *74:* words Copyright Ann Sutcliffe, music reprinted by permission of Lindsay Music, 23 Hitchin Street, Biggleswade, Beds SG18 8AX; *75:* words and music reproduced by permission of Stainer & Bell Ltd, *76:* words reproduced by permission of Stainer & Bell Ltd, music reprinted by permission of Lindsay Music; *77:* words by Geoffrey Gardner, music reprinted by permission of Lindsay Music; *78:* words by David Self reprinted with his permission, music reprinted by permission of Lindsay Music; *79:* words by Geoffrey Gardner, music reprinted by permission of Lindsay Music; *80:* words and music by Simon Fitter, used with his permission; *81:* words (c) Arthur Scholey, music by Donald Swann reprinted by permission of Lindsay Music; *82:* words and music reproduced by permission of Stainer & Bell Limited; *83* and *85:* words by Geoffrey Gardner, music reprinted by permission of Lindsay Music; *86:* words and music reproduced by permission of Stainer & Bell Ltd; *87:* words by Geoffrey Gardner, music by David Lynch (NYC); *88:* words (c) Arthur Scholey, music reprinted by permission of Lindsay Music; *89:* words and music by David Stoll; *90:* words and music reproduced by permission of Stainer & Bell Ltd; *91:* words by Geoffrey Gardner, music reprinted by permission of Lindsay Music; *92:* words by Geoffrey Gardner; *93:* words and music by Jill Darby, printed by permission of BTW Music; *94:* music reproduced by permission of Stainer & Bell Ltd; *96:* Copyright words and music by Jancis Harvey; *98:* words and music by Stuart Dauermann and Steffi Geiser Rubin, (c) 1975 Lillenas Publishing Company. All rights reserved. Used by permission; *99:* words and music (c) 1985 Patrick Appleford; *100:* words by Ronald H. Green. Copyright Kevin Mayhew Ltd. Used by permission from Hymns Old and New, Licence No. 884082, music by John Edward Jones; *101:* words by Geoffrey Gardner, music reprinted by permission of Lindsay Music; *102:* words and music used by permission of Salvationist Publishing & Supplies Ltd; *103:* Copyright words and music Jancis Harvey; *104:* words and music, reproduced by permission of Stainer & Bell Ltd; *105:* extra words by Geoffrey Gardner; *106:* words by Geoffrey Gardner, music reprinted by permission of Lindsay Music; *109:* words and music by Susan Sayers. Copyright by Kevin Mayhew Ltd. Used by permission from Hymns and Old and New, Licence No. 884081; *111:* words by Geoffrey Gardner, music reprinted by permission of Lindsay Music; *112:* words and music by Alison Carver; *113:* (To everything there is a season) Words from the Book of Ecclesiastes. Adaptation and music by Peter Seeger. (c) 1962 Melody Trails Inc. Assigned to TRO Essex Music Ltd; *114:* words and music by Geoffrey Gardner; *115:* words (c) Arthur Scholey and music by Donald Swann reprinted by permission of Lindsay Music; *117:* words by Elizabeth Bennett, music by Colin Evans; *118:* words (c) Arthur Scholey, music by John Edward Jones; *119:* music by Geoffrey Gardner, with simplified arrangement by Douglas Coombes, printed by permission of Oxford University Press; *120:* words by Cecily Taylor, music by Richard Graves by permission of Novello & Company Ltd; *122:* words by Geoffrey Gardner; *124:* words and music by Pete Ratcliffe, (c) Pete Ratcliffe/Jubilate Hymns; *125:* words and music by Sydney Carter, (c) 1963 TRO Essex Music Ltd, 19–20 Poland Street, London W1V 3DD. International Copyright secured. All rights reserved. Used by permission; *126:* Copyright words and music reproduced by permission of Stainer & Bell Limited; *129:* words reproduced by permission of Stainer & Bell Ltd, music reprinted by permission of Lindsay Music; *131:* words by J M C Crum, printed by permission of Oxford University Press; *132:* words by Alan Dale, printed by permission of Oxford University Press; *133:* Copyright words and music Jancis Harvey; *134:* words (c) Arthur Scholey, music by John Edward Jones; *135:* words by Rev Paul Booth with his permission to change the words as required, music reprinted by permission of Lindsay Music; *136:* words and music by Robert Smith; *137:* words and music (c) Estelle White 1984. Used with permission; *138:* words by Alex Mitchell, with permission from Leadership Today; *139:* words (c) Arthur Scholey, music reprinted by permission of Lindsay Music; *140:* words adapted from Sanskrit by Satish Kumar, music by Donald Swann; *141:* words adapated by Geoffrey Gardner; *143:* music by John Edward Jones; *145:* words and music by Roger Courtney (c) Roger Courtney; *146:* words and music reproduced by permission of Stainer & Bell Ltd; *147:* words and music by Sebastian Temple. Copyright Sebastian Temple/Franciscan Communications, USA; *148:* words by Geoffrey Gardner.

Published at the request of the
Educational Broadcasting Council by
BBC Books, a division of
BBC Enterprises Limited,
Woodlands, 80 Wood Lane,
London W12 0TT.
First published 1988. Reprinted 1988, 1989, 1992
© BBC Enterprises Ltd 1988

ISBN 0 563 34249 8

Origination by Computerised Typesetting Services

Printed and bound by Bell and Bain Ltd., Glasgow

4

Contents

Introduction

I hope that you enjoy using the songs in *Come and Praise 2*. It has been compiled in response to requests from schools and churches to extend the range of material in the first *Come and Praise* anthology. You'll find sections on the seasons, on festivals such as Harvest, Christmas and Easter, on the stewardship of the world's resources, on peace and on many of the concerns which form part of the lives of children and adults.

Come and Praise 1 was compiled in 1978 simply to provide hymns, or songs as I prefer to call them, to enable listeners to *Together* (BBC School Radio's assembly programme for primary schools) to join in with the singing. Then it became widely used throughout the week in schools and at weekends in Sunday schools and churches. With sales of over 2 million copies in 10 years, it has made an enormous impact on assemblies.

Come and Praise 1 and *2* have their roots in the Judaeo–Christian tradition. In compiling them I have borne in mind that, whilst many of those using the songs will have begun to explore the dimension of faith, many will not have embraced any particular faith for themselves. Some will be at home with worship, some will be crossing the threshold of worship and some will be looking in on worship, perhaps for the first time.

Most of the songs celebrate the activity of God in the world and many remind us of our responsibilities to care for it in partnership. An innovation in *Come and Praise 2* will appeal to those who reflect the festivals of many faiths in their school assemblies: alternative words are sometimes suggested to enable the songs to be adapted for whatever festival is current.

The music of the books is, above all, singable. It has been called the 'music of the people', which I suppose means that it has more links with the tunes people have in the past sung outside formal places of worship. This isn't to say that all the items lend themselves to a full-throated delivery; many are quietly reflective, such as 'Mother Teresa's Prayer', which has been arranged in two echoing parts. The variety ranges from rounds to spirituals. Melodies are predominantly European, but Africa, Asia, the Middle East and the Caribbean are also represented.

I would like to thank all the teachers, education advisers and children who have suggested the shape which *Come and Praise 2* has taken. I especially appreciate the patience of my own children — Andrew, Stephen, Paul and Anna — who for months have put up with my attempts to sing and play hundreds of hymns in my search for material. I am grateful to John Jones, the project's researcher, and to Duxha Patel, my assistant, for their painstaking work. My particular thanks are due to Douglas Coombes, for his invaluable advice on the music and for his splendid arrangements of the songs. At the centre of the project are the *Together* listeners: they brought *Come and Praise* into being and this second book is, above all, for them. I hope that the songs of *Come and Praise 2* will, together with the first book, go far beyond the broadcasts in which they are heard, and into the daily experiences of every child and adult who sings them.

Geoffrey Marshall-Taylor
BBC School Radio
Broadcasting House
London

Arrangements

The arrangements of the hymns in this collection are similar to those in the first *Come and Praise* book. The piano accompaniment contains the melody in all the hymns except for the special version of *The holly and the ivy* (page 86).

The accompaniments have been simplified, where copyright allows, in order to make the arrangements accessible for widely ranging pianistic abilities. Many pianists will wish to elaborate to suit their own technique and the style of the item. All the arrangements should be regarded as material to be used and adapted according to the ability of all concerned, as well as the availability of instruments.

A part for melodic instruments is printed above the piano part. This may be played by such instruments as a descant recorder, violin, flute, oboe, glockenspiel or xylophone. Space does not allow for any of these parts to be written out for Bb instruments such as clarinets or trumpets. However, if these instruments are available, the melodic instrumental part should be written out a whole tone higher.

Chord symbols have been printed above the melodic instrument stave. These symbols are not just for guitarists, but may be used as a guide for improvising accompaniments on instruments such as piano, organ and other electronic keyboards. A symbol chart for guitarists is given overleaf.

Introductions to the songs

Introductions for the hymns can be devised in various ways such as:
1 Playing the whole hymn;
2 Playing just the verse or the chorus (where applicable);
3 Playing the first and/or last phrase.

In a number of hymns, especially quicker and rhythmic ones, having a 2–4 bar link between verses will allow the singers to be ready with the words. Links will also give singers a chance to take a breath and so be ready to start the new verse confidently. These links can often be the last phrase, repeated by the accompanying instruments.

Rounds

Care must be taken that rounds do not become an opportunity for groups to out-shout each other. Before singing in parts, always make sure that the round is really known and that it can be sung confidently and unaccompanied.

Ideally, the next stage is for the round to be sung in two parts, with the children starting, and the teacher coming in second. The teacher should enter at various places if it is a 3 or 4 part round. When the children can confidently sing the round in this way, the roles should be reversed with the teacher starting and the children entering at one of the other various places. When this can be sung, the children can divide into two groups, and then, where applicable, three and four groups.

Children must hear all the parts of the round blending together. They should never cover their ears. Quiet singing is to be encouraged, which will enable the children to hear and enjoy the harmonies.

Rounds can end in two ways:

1 Each group sings the round a number of predetermined times, which will give a tapering off effect.
2 All groups end together at the end of their respective phrase, with a pause on the last note. The round will therefore end on a satisfying chord.

Percussion

Unpitched percussion instruments, such as drums, tambourines and triangles, could be added to many of the hymns: improvisation should be simple, especially when accompanying broadcasts, so that the vocal line is not swamped.

Douglas Coombes

Guitar Chords

The numbers refer to the fingers to be used (e.g. 1 means the first finger)
*signifies strings not to be used

A
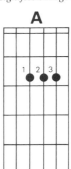

A7
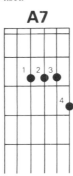

Am7
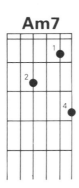

Am

Ab

B7
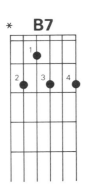

Bm

Bb
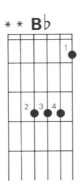

Bbmaj7
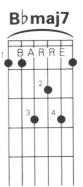

C
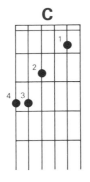

C7
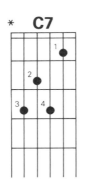

Cm

C#

C#maj7

C#dim7
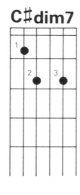

C#m

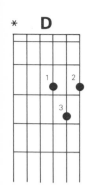

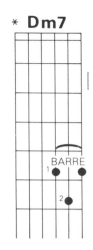

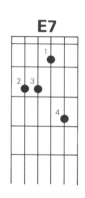

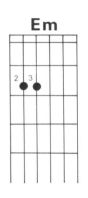

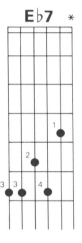

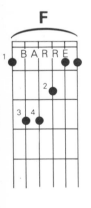

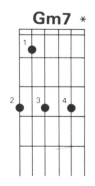

73

When your Father made the world

Gently and lightly

1 When your fa - ther made the world, be - fore that world was old,

In his eye what he had made was love - ly to be - hold, Help your

peo - ple to care for your world. *Chorus* The world is a gar - den you made, And

you are the one who plant - ed the seed, The world is a gar - den you made, A

life for our food, life for our joy, Life we could kill _____ with our sel - fish greed.

2 And the world that he had made, the seas, the rocks, the air,
All the creatures and the plants he gave into our care.
Help your people to care for your world.
Chorus

3 When you walked in Galilee, you said your Father knows
When each tiny sparrow dies, each fragile lily grows.
Help your people to care for your world.
Chorus

4 And the children of the earth, like sheep within your fold,
Should have food enough to eat, and shelter from the cold.
Help your people to care for your world.
Chorus

Words: Ann Conlon   Music: Peter Rose
This was written for the World Wide Fund for Nature.

14

Sad, puzzled eyes

Gentle moving

1 Sad, puz-zled eyes of small hun-gry child-ren, Thin, wea-ry bod-ies tend-ing the ground;

Weak, plead-ing voi-ces beg-ging in cit-ies, They long for the day when food is shared round.

Chorus

Prayers of sor-row, prayers of lov-ing, Look-ing for ways to give and to share.

Learn-ing, ex-plain-ing, help-ing, sup-port-ing, Show all the world how deep-ly we care.

2 Rumbling earthquakes, villages topple;
Drought shrivels cattle, harvests and men,
Flood waters swirling, drowning and surging,
Despairing survivors begin life again.
Chorus

3 Terror and death in war shattered countries,
Misery, tears, deep longing for peace.
Refugees flee — no hope for the future;
How long must they wait for suffering to cease?
Chorus

Words: Ann Sutcliffe   Music: Douglas Coombes

75

Bread for the world

Not too fast

1 I saw the Man from Ga - li - lee Who told a mes - sage new. The

hun - gry ground had ga - thered round, To see what he could do. And

in his words was hope; And in his hands was bread. 'Come

share this bread, And share my life— My life for you,' he said.

CODA (after v.4)

Yet Je - sus shows us hope, For in his hands is bread; Bread

for the world, If all will share- He is the liv - ing bread.____

2 I saw a boy with barley loaves;
   He had some small fish too.
   'I can't do much, but I can share:
   Lord Jesus, it's for you.
   For in your words is hope
   And in your hands is bread.
   I'll share my bread,
   And know your love —
   Your life for me,' he said.

3 I saw a rich young man, who came
   To speak to Jesus too.
   'I want to live, I don't know how,'
   He said, 'What can I do?'
   And Jesus answered, 'This
   Is life, to share your bread.
   Sell all you have,
   Give to the poor,
   Life can be yours,' he said.

4 I saw the whole world in the eyes
   Of one small hungry boy.
   There is no hope, there is no life,
   There is no sign of joy.
   And how can there be hope,
   Where people have no bread?
   They struggle on,
   And try to live,
   But life hangs by a thread.
      Yet Jesus shows us hope,
      For in his hands is bread;
      Bread for the world,
      If all will share:
      He is the living bread.

Words and music: George A. Chalmers

76
God in his love

With a lilt

1 God in his love for us lent us this pla-net, Gave it a pur-pose in time and in space: Small as a spark from the fire of cre-a-tion, Cra-dle of life and the home of our race.

2 Thanks be to God for its bounty and beauty,
Life that sustains us in body and mind:
Plenty for all, if we learn how to share it,
Riches undreamed of to fathom and find.

3 Long have the wars of man ruined its harvest:
Long has earth bowed to the terror of force:
Long have we wasted what others have need of,
Poisoned the fountain of life at its source.

4 Earth is the Lord's: it is ours to enjoy it.
Ours, as his stewards, to farm and defend.
From its pollution, misuse, and destruction.
Good Lord, deliver us, world without end!

Words: Fred Pratt Green   Music: Douglas Coombes

Desert rain

For the full score, see the next page.

1 The sun burns hot and dry,
  High in the cloudless sky,
  No shade.
  The soil is crumbling dust,
  Like powder at the touch.

2 The brittle corn is crushed,
  Away blow empty husks,
  No food.
  No life left in the grain,
  The seed has failed again.

3 Empty hands, reaching out,
  But there's nothing there.
  Cracking lips,
  Withered skin,
  The eyes just stare.

4 The cows and goats are thin,
  The bones show through the skin,
  No milk.
  They search for grass to graze,
  They swelter in the haze.

5 The wells are empty holes,
  The river only stones,
  No drink.
  When will a storm cloud burst
  To satisfy the thirst?

6 Then it came, cooling rain,
  Falling all around;
  Everywhere,
  Muddy pools, form in the ground.

7 The desert dances on,
  Now water has come down,
  New life.
  And seeds of hope begin.
  How long will be the spring?
  How long will be the spring?

Words: Geoffrey Gardner   Music: Douglas Coombes

20

Desert rain

* Play Right Hand an octave higher.

Words: Geoffrey Gardner   Music: Douglas Coombes

78

The song of St Francis

1 By bro-ther sun who brings the day ___ And sheds his dazz-ling ___ light ___ And warms the world with_ wel-come ray;_ By sis-ter moon and sis-ter stars Who turn through-out the night ___ A-bove in hea-ven as they shine: Be praised by all_ your_ crea-tures, Lord, To

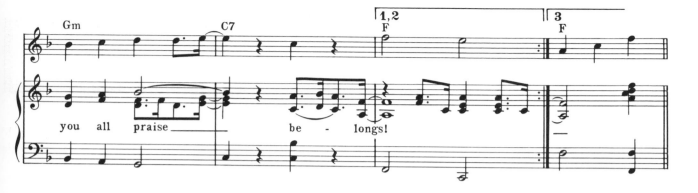

you all praise_____ be - longs!

2 By brother wind and brother air
   On cloudy days and bright,
   In weather stormy, calm or fair;
   By sister water, precious pure,
   Whose taste is cool delight —
   Most humble yet reviving drink:
   Be praised by all your creatures, Lord,
   To you all praise belongs!

3 By brother fire, robust and strong,
   Who gives us heat and might,
   With you now join we all our song,
   And with our sister earth as well,
   With whom we all unite
   To sing with flowers, fruit and grass:
   Be praised by all your creatures, Lord,
   To you all praise belongs!

Words: David Self   Music: Douglas Coombes
This is based on a poem by St Francis of Assisi.

79

From the tiny ant

With an easy swing

No one else will care for them,(1) It's up(2) it's up(1 & 2) it's up to you._____

2 (1) From the tabby cat,
   (2) *From the tabby cat,*
   (1) To the desert rat,
   (2) *To the desert rat,*
   (1) From the hamster to the chimpanzee,
   (2) *From the hamster to the chimpanzee,*
   (1) From the common tern,
   (2) *From the common tern,*
   (1) To the crawling worm,
   (2) *To the crawling worm,*
   (1) Care for them, it's up to me,
   (2) *Care for them, it's up to me,*
   (1 & 2) Care for them, it's up to me,
   (1 & 2) Care for them, it's up to me.
   (1 & 2) No one else will care for them,
   (1) It's up
   (2) *It's up*
   (1 & 2) It's up to me.

3 (1) From the mongrel dog,
   (2) *From the mongrel dog,*
   (1) To the snorting hog,
   (2) *To the snorting hog,*
   (1) From the badger to the platypus,
   (2) *From the badger to the platypus,*
   (1) From the small minnow,
   (2) *From the small minnow,*
   (1) To the white rhino,
   (2) *To the white rhino,*
   (1) Care for them, it's up to us,
   (2) *Care for them, it's up to us,*
   (1 & 2) Care for them, it's up to us,
   (1 & 2) Care for them, it's up to us.
   (1 & 2) No one else will care for them,
   (1) It's up
   (2) *It's up*
   (1 & 2) It's up to us.

Words: Geoffrey Gardner   Music: Douglas Coombes
This song can be sung by two groups, indicated by (1) and (2). Generally, group (2) echoes
group (1). If you prefer, everyone can sing every line.

80
All the animals

Jauntily

1 All the a-ni-mals that I have ev-er seen, Big ones, lit-tle ones, and o-thers in be-tween, Four legs, two legs, Some no legs at all; I like them all.

2 All the animals that like your strokes and pats,
   Dogs and hamsters, gerbils, guinea pigs and cats,
   Mice and tortoises,
   Rabbits in the hutch;
   I like so much.

3 All the animals that fly up in the sky,
   Robins, wrens, and butterflies that flutter by,
   Magpies, dragonflies,
   And the bumble bee;
   I like to see.

4 All the animals I only see at night,
   Hedgehog, nightingale and owl with eyes so bright,
   Fox and badger,
   Moth and bat and shrew;
   I like them too.

5 All the animals that live beneath the sea,
Shrimps and prawns and jellyfish that tickle me,
Starfish, anemonies,
Crabs beneath my feet!
I like to meet.

6 There are animals I'll never see at all,
Some live overseas, and some are just too small,
All God's animals,
Need the care we give
If they're to live.

Words and music: Simon Fitter

81

What about being old Moses?

Rag-time

1 What a-bout be-ing old Mo-ses And slog-ging a-cross the sand, Es-cap-ing through the wil-der-ness To reach the Pro-mised Land? To be old Mo-ses would be a mis-take To-day the fun of it is That we've on-ly one world and we can make Our Pro-mised Land from this.

2 What about being Saint Brendon,
For mile after nautical mile,
He plunged across fantastic seas
In search of the Blessed Isle?

To be Saint Brendon would be a mistake;
Today the fun of it is
That we've only one world and we can make
Our blessed isle from this!

3 What about being Columbus
And seeking another way round,
With oceans still to voyage on,
And more new worlds to be found?

To be Columbus would be a mistake;
Today the fun of it is
That we've only one world and we can make
Our new world out of this!

4 What about taking a space-ship
And flying to space unknown.
There must be worlds enough to give
Us each one of his own?

To take a space-ship would be a mistake;
Today the fun of it is
That we've only one world and we can make
Our one world out of this!

Words: Arthur Scholey   Music: Donald Swann
St Brendon (484–577 A.D.) was an Irish Christian who sailed
for several years to find 'paradise amid the waves'. Christopher
Columbus (1451–1506) was an Italian explorer.

It's the springs

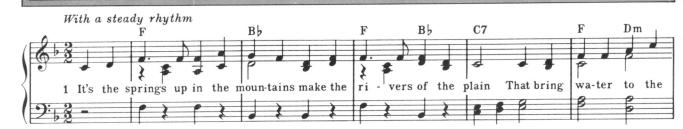

With a steady rhythm

1 It's the springs up in the moun-tains make the ri - vers of the plain That bring wa-ter to the

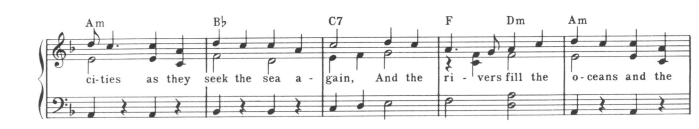

ci-ties as they seek the sea a - gain, And the ri - vers fill the o-ceans and the

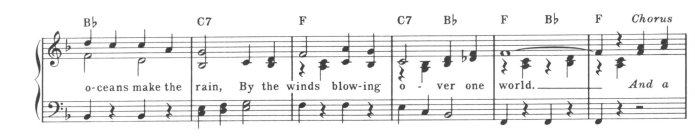

o-ceans make the rain, By the winds blow-ing o - ver one world. _____ And a

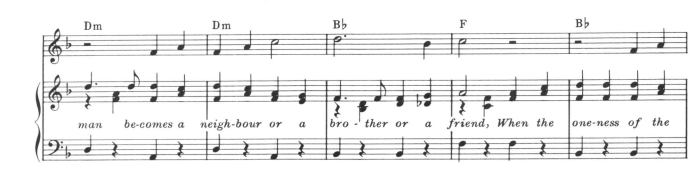

man be-comes a neigh-bour or a bro-ther or a friend, When the one-ness of the

world you un-der - stand. _____ And the East for your neigh-bour is an-

o-ther neigh-bour's West, It de - pends up - on just where you stand.

2 There are people in the mountains and the valleys down below,
  There are people in the tropics, there are people in the snow,
  Some are happy, some are homeless folk who have no place to go,
  But we all have to live in one world.
  Chorus

3 There are workers for their wages out in field and factory,
  There are fishers for our food supply in boats upon the sea;
  There are people still imprisoned in the cage of poverty,
  As we labour for life in one world.
  Chorus

4 As the sun lights up the morning, and another day is found,
  It's a gift to all that's living, that the world still spins around,
  And the night is still the day but seen the other way around,
  As the sun shines upon this one world.
  Chorus

Words and music: Richard Tysoe

I'm going to paint

83

Smooth and flowing

Chorus

I'm going to paint a per-fect pic-ture, A world of make be-lieve;

No more hun-ger, war or suf-fer-ing, The world I like to see.

The world I like to see, The world I like to see.

Verse

1 The black-bird sings in the hedge-row, The white owl sleeps in the barn, The brown geese fly— a group in the sky, The yel-low chick pecks the corn. I'm

Chorus

2 The stream runs clear through the meadow,
  The wheat ears swell with the grain,
  The oak trees give them shelter and shade,
  The sunlight bursts through the rain.
  Chorus

3 The farmers gather the harvest,
  The children play by the mill,
  The cattle chew and flick up their tails,
  The ponies graze on the hill.

  Chorus:
  I'm going to paint a perfect picture,
  A world of make believe;
  No more hunger, war or suffering,
  The world I'd like to see,
  The world I'd like to see.

  Words: Geoffrey Gardner   Music: Douglas Coombes
  This song describes a world where all races (verse 1),
  all the world's resources (verse 2) and all the world's
  creatures (verse 3) are in perfect harmony.

84
Waves are beating

2 God has made the sea so vast,
Ocean's roaring swell;
Cliffs of chalk and granite rocks,
Sailors know them well;
Furl the sails and winch the sheets,
Feel the salt spray fly,
Know the freedom of the sea,
Underneath the sky.

3 Ever since the world began,
People sailed the seas,
Plunged across the roaring tides,
Floated on the breeze;
Feel the decks beneath your feet,
See the golden sand,
Set your feet upon the shore,
Coming home to land.

Copyright controlled

85
Spirit of peace

Gently – with movement

1 Spi - rit of peace, come to our wait - ing world, Through - out the na - tions, may your voice be heard, Un - lock the door of hope, for you hold the key;

CODA (after last verse)

Spi - rit of peace, come to our world. Spi - rit of God, come to our world.

rall.

2 Spirit of love, come to our waiting world;
Throughout the nations, may your voice be heard.
Unlock the door of hope, for you hold the key;
Spirit of love, come to our world.

3 Spirit of strength, come to our waiting world;
Throughout the nations, may your voice be heard.
Unlock the door of hope, for you hold the key;
Spirit of strength, come to our world.

4 Spirit of light, come to our waiting world;
Throughout the nations, may your voice be heard.
Unlock the door of hope, for you hold the key;
Spirit of light, come to our world.

5 Spirit of God, come to our waiting world;
Throughout the nations, may your voice be heard.
Unlock the door of hope, for you hold the key;
Spirit of God, come to our world.
Spirit of God, come to our world.

Words: Geoffrey Gardner   Music: Douglas Coombes

86
The bell of creation

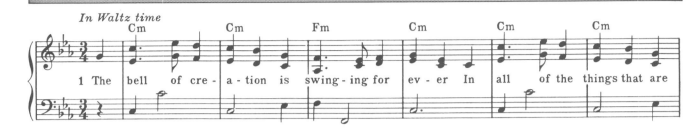

In Waltz time

1 The bell of cre-a-tion is swing-ing for ev-er In all of the things that are

com-ing to be, ____ The bell of cre-a-tion is swing-ing for

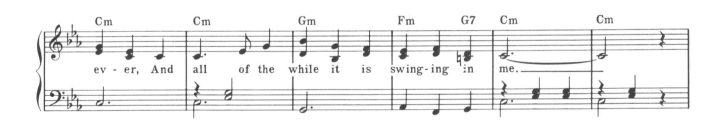

ev-er, And all of the while it is swing-ing in me. ____

Chorus

Swing, bell, ov-er the land! Swing, bell,

un-der the sea! The bell of cre-a-tion is swing-ing for

ev - er, And all of the while it is swing-ing in me.

2 In all of my loving, in all of my labour,
In all of the things that are coming to be,
In all of my loving, in all of my labour,
The bell of creation is swinging in me.
Chorus

3 I look to the life that is living for ever
In all of the things that are coming to be,
I look to the life that is living for ever
And all of the while it is looking for me.
Chorus

4 I'll swing with the bell that is swinging for ever,
In all of the things that are coming to be,
I'll swing with the bell that is swinging for ever,
And all of the while it is swinging in me.
Chorus

Words and music: Sydney Carter

40

87
Give us hope, Lord

With quiet joy

1 Give us hope, Lord, for each day,

Give us hope, Lord, for each day.

Guide our footsteps on the way,

Give us hope, Lord, for each day.

2 Give us strength, Lord, for each day . . .

3 Give us peace, Lord, for each day . . .

4 Give us love, Lord, for each day . . .

5 Give us joy, Lord, for each day . . .

Alternative words

1 Give us friends, Lord, for each day,
Give us friends, Lord, for each day,
Make us thankful on the way,
Give us friends, Lord, for each day.

2 Give us food, Lord, for each day . . .

3 Give us homes, Lord, for each day . . .

4 Give us clothes, Lord, for each day . . .

Words: Geoffrey Gardner   Music: David Lynch

*This song was written as an expression
of praise through the use of bells and other
percussion instruments such as triangles and
Indian bells. A set of keys or a few coins
can be 'jingled' together. Get the singers to
make up a percussion part.*

*It would be effective to turn the melodic
instrumental part into a second part
for a small group of singers.*

*The words by Geoffrey Gardner appear with the agreement of
David Lynch, the composer of the music. David Lynch has
requested that his original words, known as 'The Bell Song' be
printed in addition.*

The Bell Song

1 You gotta have love in your heart;
You gotta have love in your heart;
You knew it was Jesus right from the start;
You gotta have love in your heart.

2 You gotta have peace on you mind;
You gotta have peace on your mind;
You knew it was Jesus there all the time;
You gotta have peace on your mind.

3 You gotta have joy in your soul;
You gotta have joy in your soul;
The love of Jesus will make you whole;
You gotta have peace in your soul.

David Lynch

88

I was lying in the roadway

Flowing tempo

Dm / Dm / Dm

1 I was ly-ing in the road-way, Beat-en

Dm / Bb / A7

robbed and left to die, When some-one passed the o-ther side— I—

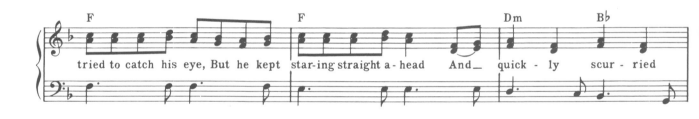

F / F / Dm / Bb

tried to catch his eye, But he kept star-ing straight a-head And— quick-ly scur-ried

A7 / D / Bm / F#m

by. Was that you, my friend, Was that you? Was that

G / D / D / Bm

you, my friend, Was that you? Oh, I real-ly was in—

2 I was crying in the roadway,
  Freezing cold and gripped in pain,
  Then someone came across to see —
  I dared to hope again;
  But he just looked and hurried on
  And left me in the rain.
    Was that you, my friend,
    Was that you?
    Was that you, my friend,
    Was that you?
    Oh, I really was in need —
    Was that you?
    Was that you?

3 I was dying in the roadway,
  And at last I knew despair,
  For now, I saw with fading eyes,
  My enemy stood there —
  But then he knelt, and lifted me,
  And brought me safely here.
    That was you, my friend,
    That was you!
    That was you, my friend,
    That was you!
    Oh, you were a friend in deed —
    That was you!
    That was you!

Words: Arthur Scholey   Music: Douglas Coombes
A song based on the parable of the Good Samaritan
(Luke 10.)

44

89 Guess how I feel

At a gentle pace

1 Guess how I feel,__ some - times— No-thing is real,__
  Know what I think,__ some - times— I've lost the link,__

some - times. Ev-'ry - one's liv - ing in dreams.
some - times. No-thing makes sense, so it seems.

We've all be-come strange ma-chines. But then I | *1st time only* | *Look in the sky,*__

Chorus

Tell all the clouds to pass on by.__ The sun will be there E-ven if you can't see__ it,

2 How about you,
  Sometimes?
  Are you lost, too,
  Sometimes?
  Caught up in roundabout schemes?
  Gives this a try
  Sometimes,
  Set your sights high
  Sometimes,
  Simply try changing the scene,
  I'm sure you know what I mean.

  Chorus
  Look in the sky,
  Tell all the clouds to pass on by.
  The sun will be there
  Even if you can't see it,
  Always be there,
  I can guarantee it,
  Every time.

  Words and music: David Stoll

90

I come like a beggar

2 I come like a prisoner to bring you the key,
I come like a prisoner to bring you the key.
By the hungry I will feed you,
By the poor I'll make you rich,
By the broken I will mend you.
Tell me,
Which one is which?

3 The need of another is the gift that I bring,
The need of another is the gift that I bring.
By the hungry I will feed you,
By the poor I'll make you rich,
By the broken I will mend you.
Tell me,
Which one is which?

4 Take the wine that I bring you and the bread that I break,
Take the wine that I bring you and the bread that I break.
By the hungry I will feed you,
By the poor I'll make you rich,
By the broken I will mend you.
Tell me,
Which one is which?

Words and music: Sydney Carter

91
Break out

With a strong Rock beat

1 You can build a wall a-round___ you, Stone by stone, a so-lid ring;___
You can live a-lone, in an emp-ty home, Be in charge and be the king.___

Chorus

Break out,___ reach out,___ Make the walls crum-ble down, down, down.

Break out,___ reach out,___ Make the walls tum-ble down.

2 You can build a wall around you,
  Stop the sun from shining in;
  There'll be snow-topped trees and a chilling breeze,
  Always winter, never spring.
  Chorus

3 You can build a wall around you,
  Slam the door shut fast and firm;
  There's no friend at hand who can understand,
  To love you and help you learn.
  Chorus

Words: Geoffrey Gardner   Music: Douglas Coombes
This is based on Oscar Wilde's story 'The selfish giant'.

92

When night arrives

Steadily – with a lilt

1 When night ar - rives — and chills the skies, — And still - ness set - tles a - cross the land, The ha - zy moon — shines in the gloom — And sha - dows shud - der close at hand.

Chorus

Sing, sing — our prai - ses bring, — The dawn lights up — the dis - tant east,

Sing, sing — our prai - ses bring, — The sun — will come in its glo - ry.

2 No sound is heard from sleeping birds,
  And frost is white on the roads and grass;
  There are no signs of warmer times,
  No buds to show that winter's passed.
  Chorus

3 When darkest fears and thoughts appear,
  The clouds are grey and cheerless,
  When friends have gone, we're all alone,
  The day looks cold and lifeless.
  Chorus

Words: Geoffrey Gardner   Music: Traditional (Greensleeves)

93
Morning sun

Gently and rhythmically

1 Morn-ing sun,__ morn-ing sun,__ Lights the day__ that's just be-gun,__

Help-ing ev - 'ry - one to see__ How beau-ti-ful__ the world can be.__

1,2,3

4 ter-nal-ly.__

2 Midday sun, midday sun,
   All the warmest light has come,
   Brightening our lives below,
   Helping all the plants to grow.

3 Setting sun, setting sun,
   When the day is nearly done,
   Moving all the light away,
   Till you rise another day.

4 Shining sun, shining sun,
   Bringing life to everyone,
   Helping all the world to see,
   You shine on us eternally.

Words and music: Jill Darby

94
Mother Teresa's prayer

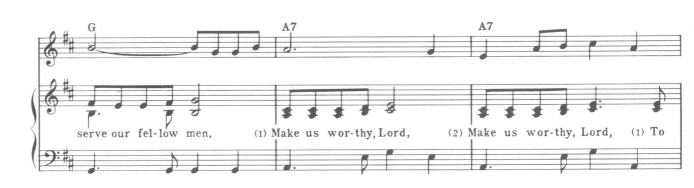

2 (1) Give them, through our hands,
  (2) *Give them, through our hands,*
  (1) This day, their daily bread,
  (2) *This day, their daily bread.*
  (1) Give them, through our hands,
  (2) *Give them, through our hands,*
  (1) This day, their daily bread,
  (2) *This day, their daily bread.*
  (1) And by our understanding love,
  (2) *And by our understanding love,*
  (1) Give peace and joy,
  (2) *Give peace and joy,*
  (1) Give peace and joy,
  (2) *Give peace and joy.*

Short version

1 Make us worthy, Lord,
  To serve our fellow men;
  Make us worthy, Lord,
  To serve our fellow men,
  Throughout the world who live and die,
  In poverty and hunger,
  In poverty and hunger.

2 Give them, through our hands,
  This day, their daily bread;
  Give them, through our hands,
  This day, their daily bread,
  And by our understanding love,
  Give peace and joy,
  Give peace and joy.

Words: Traditional   Music: Donald Swann
This is often known as 'Mother Teresa's daily prayer'. The song can be sung by two groups,
indicated by (1) and (2). Group (2) echoes the tune and words sung by Group (1).
Alternatively, it can be Sung without the echoing line.

Rejoice in the Lord always

Words and music: Traditional
This is based on Philippians 4:4. The song may be sung as a round.

96
A still small voice

With an easy swing

1 A still small voice in the heart of the ci-ty, A still small voice on the moun-tain, Through the storms that are rag-ing— or the qui-et of the eve-ning, It can on-ly be heard if you lis-ten.—

2 The voice of God in a place that is troubled,
The voice of God in the dawn,
Through noise of the shouting, through the still sound of the sleeping,
It can only be heard if you listen.

3 Give time to hear, give us love to listen,
Give wisdom for understanding,
There's a still, small voice which to each one is speaking,
If we only have the time to listen.

Words and music: Jancis Harvey
This is based on words from 1 Kings 19:12.

97
Simple gifts

Traditional. A Shaker song. The melody of 'Lord of the Dance' is based on this tune.

98
You shall go out with joy

Start steadily and repeat, gradually getting faster

Words and music: Stuart Dauermann and Steffi Geiser Rubin
This is based on the words of Isaiah 55:12. The song can be repeated, getting faster each time.

56

Love will never come to an end

CODA

Love is for ev - er, for ev - er and ev - er is Love.

Chorus

2 I may seem a great success,
   Wisdom, wealth or charm possess,
   Yet whatever I achieve
   I am nothing without love.
   Chorus

3 Love is patient, love is kind.
   Love requires a truthful mind.
   Love will keep no score of wrongs.
   There is nothing love can't face.
   Chorus

4 Childish thoughts are put away,
   Partial knowledge has its day.
   Love with faith and hope endures,
   There is nothing conquers love.

   Chorus:
   Love will never come to an end,
   Love will never come to an end,
   Three things will last:
   Faith, hope and love,
   But greatest of all is love,
   Love, love, love.
   Love is forever,
   For ever and ever, is love.

   Words and music: Patrick Appleford
   This is based on words from 1 Corinthians 13.

I may speak

2 I may give all I have to neighbours,
  And explore every mansion above
  To possess all the jewels of wisdom —
  I am nothing at all, without love;
  Chorus

3 By my faith I may move the mountains,
  And may stand for a cause to be won;
  If I do not have love in doing —
  Then I shall be the better by none;
  Chorus

4 Now this loving is kind and generous,
  And a wonderful, glorious sign
  Of the limitless, deep, compassion
  From the Power, supremely divine;
  Chorus

Words: Ronald Green   Music: John Jones
This is based on words from 1 Corinthians 13.

101

In the bustle of the city

With excitement

1 In the bus-tle of the ci-ty, There is life, there is love;____ In the

bird-song of the coun-try, There is life, there is love;____ Down the

streets and down the lanes, Through the wind and through the flames, Where the hu-man heart is beat-ing,

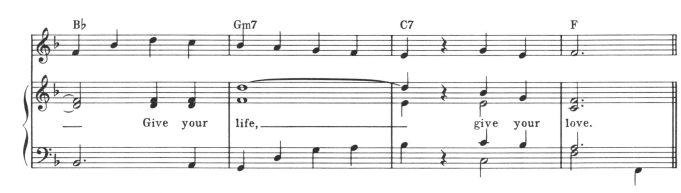

____ Give your life,____ give your love.

2 Where the voices lift in laughter,
   There is life, there is love;
   Where the tears fall from the crying,
   There is life, there is love;
   During health and during pain,
   Through the sunshine, through the rain,
   Where the human heart is beating,
   Give your life, give your love.

3 See the families, see the lonely,
   There is life, there is love;
   With the sheltered, with the homeless,
   There is life, there is love;
   To the young and to the old,
   Through the warm and through the cold,
   Where the human heart is beating,
   Give your life, give your love.

4 In the factory and garden,
   There is life, there is love,
   For the worker and the jobless,
   There is life, there is love;
   To all men and to all women,
   Through their dying and their living,
   Where the human heart is beating,
   Give your life, give your love.

Words: Geoffrey Gardner   Music: Douglas Coombes

102

You can't stop rain

Sprightly

1 You can't stop rain from fall-ing down, Pre-vent the sun from shin - ing. You can't stop spring from com-ing in, Or win-ter from re - sign - ing, Or still the waves or stay the winds, Or keep the day from dawn - ing; You can't stop God from lov-ing you, His love is new each morn - ing.

2 You can't stop ice from being cold,
   You can't stop fire from burning,
   Or hold the tide that's going out,
   Delay its sure returning,
   Or halt the progress of the years,
   The flight of fame and fashion;
   You can't stop God from loving you,
   His nature is compassion.

3 You can't stop God from loving you,
   Though you may have ignored him,
   You can't stop God from loving you,
   However you betray him;
   From love like this no power on earth
   The human heart can sever,
   You can't stop God from loving you,
   Not God, not now, nor ever.

Words: John Gowans   Music: J. Larson

103

I am planting my feet

Chorus
With a swing

I am plant-ing my feet in the foot-steps That are there be-fore me ev-'ry day.

Tak-ing my jour-ney one step at a time The foot-steps will guide me all the way.

Verse

1 The road of life lies be-fore me— And I know that's the way I must tread. But I

have the — signs there to guide me,— And my path be-fore is clear a-head. I am

Chorus

2 There are turnings that sometimes look brighter,
And ways that seem better to me.
And people who'd stop me from travelling,
But I'll keep to the footsteps I see.
Chorus

3 It's easy somedays to feel weary,
And tire when the journey is long;
But streams always soothe and refresh me,
And footsteps ahead lead me on.
Chorus

Words and music: Jancis Harvey

104
Time is a thing

Moving steadily

1 Time is a thing Like a bird on the wing Com-ing or go-ing a-way.

Time is a thing Like a bird on the wing Com-ing or go-ing a-way.

Com-ing or gone You're tra-vel-ling on, There's no-where you can stay.

Com-ing or gone You're tra-vel-ling on, You're al-ways on the way.

2 Love is a thing
Like a bird on the wing,
Coming or going away.
Love is a thing
Like a bird on the wing,
Coming or going away.
Coming or gone,
You're travelling on,
There's nowhere you can stay.
Coming or gone,
You're travelling on,
You're always on the way.

3 Hope is a thing
Like a bird on the wing,
Coming or going away.
Hope is a thing
Like a bird on the wing,
Coming or going away.
Coming or gone,
You're travelling on,
There's nowhere you can stay.
Coming or gone,
You're travelling on,
You're always on the way.

Words and music: Sydney Carter

105
God of the morning

Steadily – with a lilt

1 God of the morn - ing, at whose voice— The cheer - ful sun— makes haste to rise, And,

like a gi - ant, does re - joice— To run— his jour - ney through the skies.

Chorus

On, on— the blaz - ing sun,— Give a - gain— your liv - ing light,

On, on— till day is done,— Shine— a - gain— and bring new life.

2 From distant places of the east
The circuit of his race begins,
And, without weariness or rest,
Around the world he flies and shines.
Chorus

3 Just like the sun, may we complete
The tasks we have to do this day,
With ready mind and active will
Move on, with hope along our way.
Chorus

Words: Isaac Watts, with extra words by Geoffrey Gardner
Music: Traditional (Greensleeves)

106

It's a new day

Lightly – with excitement

1 It's a new day, there's hope,__ It's a new day there's scope, To face a diff'rent chal-lenge, Dis-co-ver there's no end__ To new be-gin-nings,__ To the new things we can do.

2 It's a new task, there's hope,
It's a new task, there's scope,
To face a different challenge,
Discover that there's no end
To new beginnings,
To the new things we can do.

3 It's a new skill, there's hope,
It's a new skill, there's scope . . .

4 It's a new friend, there's hope,
It's a new friend, there's scope . . .

5 It's a new year, there's hope,
It's a new year, there's scope . . .

6 It's a new week, there's hope,
It's a new week, there's scope . . .

Words: Geoffrey Gardner   Music: Douglas Coombes
Choose the verses most appropriate for your needs.

107

You've got to move

Moderate Rock tempo

1 You've got to move when the Spi-rit says move, You've got to move when the Spi-rit says move; 'Cos when the Spi-rit says move, You've got to move when the Spi-rit, Move when the Spi-rit says move.

2 You've got to sing when the spirit says sing,
You've got to sing when the spirit says sing,
'Cos when the spirit says sing,
You've got to sing when the spirit,
Sing when the spirit says sing.

3 You've got to clap when the spirit says clap,
You've got to clap when the spirit says clap,
'Cos when the spirit says clap,
You've got to clap when the spirit,
Clap when the spirit says clap.

4 You've got to shout when the spirit says shout,
You've got to shout when the spirit says shout,
'Cos when the spirit says shout,
You've got to shout when the spirit,
Shout when the spirit says shout.

5 You've got to move when the spirit says move,
You've got to move when the spirit says move,
'Cos when the spirit says move,
You've got to move when the spirit,
Move when the spirit says move.

Traditional

108

The Lord, the Lord

Joyfully

1 The Lord, the Lord, the Lord is my shep-herd, The Lord, the Lord, the Lord is my shep-herd, The Lord, the Lord, the Lord is my shep-herd, The Lord is my shep-herd and I shall not want.

2 He makes me lie down in green, green pastures,
   He makes me lie down in green, green pastures,
   He makes me lie down in green, green pastures,
   The Lord is my shepherd and I shall not want.

3 He leads me beside the still, still waters.
   He leads me beside the still, still waters.
   He leads me beside the still, still waters.
   The Lord is my shepherd and I shall not want.

Traditional, based on Psalm 23.

109

Thank you for the summer morning

With a swing

1 Thank you for the sum-mer morn-ing mist-ing in - to heat, Thank you for the di - a-monds of dew be-neath my feet, Thank you for the sil - ver where a snail has wan-dered by; Oh, we praise the name of him who made the earth and sea and sky.

earth and sea and sky.

2 Thank you for the yellow fields
of corn like waving hair;
Thank you for the red surprise
of poppies here and there;
Thank you for the blue of
an electric dragon-fly;
Oh, we praise the name
of him who made
the earth and sea and sky.

3 Thank you for the splintered light
among the brooding trees;
Thank you for the leaves that rustle
in a sudden breeze;
Thank you for the branches
and the fun of climbing high;
Oh, we praise the name
of him who made
the earth and sea and sky.

4 Thank you for the evening
as the light begins to fade,
Clouds so red and purple
that the setting sun has made;
Thank you for the shadows
as the owls come gliding by;
Oh, we praise the name
of him who made
the earth and sea and sky.

Words and music: Susan Sayers

110
Sing, people, sing

Steady March tempo

2 March, come on, march,
  Beneath the springtime arch;
  Primroses a special sight,
  Cowslips make the garden bright,
  March, come on, march,
  March, come on, march.

3 March, come on march,
  Beneath the summer arch;
  Roses in the hedges high,
  Honeysuckle climbing by,
  March, come on, march,
  March, come on, march,

4 March, come on march,
  Beneath the autumn arch;
  Hazel nuts are turning brown,
  Chestnuts too are falling down;
  March, come on, march,
  March, come on, march.

5 Sing, people, sing,
  And follow in a ring,
  Praise to God for all we do,
  Marching, seeing, hearing, too;
  Sing, people, sing,
  Sing, people, sing.

Traditional

72

Round, round, round

Chorus

2 Sticky buds on chestnut trees,
 Burst into candle flowers,
 Bronze and glistening conkers hit the ground,
 There will be more next year, we hope,
 There will be more next year.
 Chorus

3 Toads and frogs make for their ponds,
 Swim and lay their spawn.
 Twist and wriggle worm-like, changing shape
 There will be more next year, we hope,
 There will be more next year.
 Chorus

Words: Geoffrey Gardner Music: Douglas Coombes

74

112

Lay my white cloak

Flowing

1 Lay my white cloak on the ground, Spring is-n't com - ing, Spring is-n't com - ing,

Cold, cold snow fall-ing all a - round, Spring is-n't com-ing this year.

Paint the trees with my sil - ver frost, Spring is-n't com - ing, Spring is-n't com - ing,

Un - der ice the_ earth is lost, Spring is-n't com-ing this year. more.

2 My cold wind will make you frown,
   Spring isn't coming, spring isn't coming;
   Blow the chimney pots all down!
   Spring isn't coming this year.
   Breath of ice and cloak of grey,
   Spring isn't coming, spring isn't coming;
   Rattle hailstones all the day,
   Spring isn't coming this year.

3 Hear sweet birdsong fill the air,
   Spring will be coming, spring will be coming;
   Sunshine smiling everywhere,
   Spring will be coming once more.
   Through the soil the flowers peep,
   Spring will be coming, spring will be coming;
   Earth is waking from her sleep,
   Spring will be coming once more.

Words and music: Alison J. Carver
This is based on Oscar Wilde's story 'The selfish giant'.

113

To ev'rything, turn

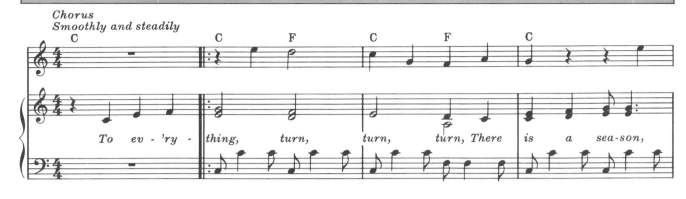

Chorus
Smoothly and steadily

To ev-'ry-thing, turn, turn, turn, There is a sea-son,

turn, turn, turn, And a time for ev-'ry pur-pose un - der hea-ven.

Verse

1 A time to be born, a time to die; A time to plant, a time to reap; A time to

kill, a time to heal, A time to laugh, a time to weep. To ev-'ry-

Chorus

2 A time to build up, a time to break down;
A time to dance, a time to mourn;
A time of love, a time of hate;
A time of war, a time of peace.
Chorus

3 A time to lose, a time to gain;
A time to tear, a time to mend;
A time to love, a time to hate;
A time for peace, I swear it's not too late.
Chorus

Words and music: Pete Seeger
This is based on the words of Ecclesiastes 3.

Flickering candles in the night

Chorus

2 Cards and streamers on the walls,
   Brighten up the room;
   Decorations, coloured lamps,
   Drive away the gloom.
   Chorus

3 Tell a story from the past;
   Celebrate in song;
   Those who changed despair to hope,
   And defeated wrong.
   Chorus

Words and music: Geoffrey Gardner
Suitable for Christmas, Hannukah and Diwali.

115
Baboushka

Steady tempo

1 'Come in, my roy-al mas-ters, I'm glad to have you stay. I wel-come you, and ask you A ques-tion, if I may? Why have you come this dis-tance From where your king-doms are? Oh, tell me, no-ble sirs, why are you jour-ney-ing so far?' 'Ba-boush-ka, oh, Ba-boush-ka, we're fol-low-ing a star. Ba-boush-ka, oh, Ba-boush-ka, we're fol-low-ing a star'.

2 'The star's a mighty marvel,
  A truly glorious sight.
  But, lords, you must stay longer —
  Oh, won't you stay the night?
  Do tell me why you hurry —
  And here's another thing:
  I marvel at the meaning of the precious gifts you bring.'

  'Baboushka, oh, Baboushka, they're for a new-born king.
  Baboushka, oh, Baboushka, they're for a new-born king.'

3 'Some king, to have such treasure,
  A star to show his birth,
  And you to do him honour,
  The greatest ones of earth —
  And yet he is a baby,
  A tiny man is he?
  O royal ones, I wonder, then, if he will welcome me?'

  'Baboushka, oh, Baboushka, oh, why not come and see?
  Baboushka, oh, Baboushka, oh, why not come and see?'

4 'I will, my royal masters —
  But not just now, I fear.
  I'll follow on tomorrow
  When I have finished here.
  My home I must make tidy,
  And sweep and polish, too,
  And then some gifts I must prepare — I have so much to do!'

  'Baboushka, oh, Baboushka, we dare not wait for you.
  Baboushka, oh, Baboushka, we dare not wait for you.'

5 At last I make the journey —
  No star to lead me on.
  Good people, can you tell me
  The way the kings have gone?
  Some shepherds tell of angels
  But now there is no sound.
  The stable, it is empty, and the baby Egypt-bound.

  'Baboushka, oh, Baboushka, we know where he is found.
  Baboushka, oh, Baboushka, we know where he is found.'

6 Through all the years I seek him
  I feel him very near
  O people, do you know him?
  Oh, tell me: Is he here?
  In all the world I travel
  But late I made my start.
  Oh, tell me if you find him for I've searched in every part.

  'Baboushka, oh, Baboushka, we find him in our heart.
  Baboushka, oh, Baboushka, we find him in our heart.'

Words: Arthur Scholey Music: Donald Swann
This is based on the Russian story of Baboushka, an old lady who, because she was too busy,
missed the chance to see the Christ Child in Bethlehem.

116

Rise up, shepherd

Joyously

1 There's a star in the east on Christ-mas morn, Rise up, shep-herd, and fol-low,___ It'll

lead to the place where the Sa-viour's born,___ Rise up, shep-herd, and fol-low.__

Leave your sheep and leave your lambs, Rise up, shep-herd, and fol-low,___

Leave your ewes and leave your rams, Rise up, shep-herd, and fol-low.__

Fol - low, fol-low,___ Rise up, shep-herd, and fol-low,___

Fol - low the star of Beth - le - hem, ___ Rise up, shep-herd, and fol-low. _

2 If you take good heed to the angel's words,
  Rise up, shepherd, and follow,
  You'll forget your flocks and forget your herds,
  Rise up, shepherd, and follow.
    Leave your sheep, and leave your lambs,
    Rise up, shepherd, and follow,
    Leave your ewes and leave your rams,
    Rise up, shepherd, and follow.
  Follow, follow,
  Rise up, shepherd, and follow,
  Follow the star of Bethlehem,
  Rise up, shepherd, and follow.

  Traditional

117

I want to see your baby boy

2 I've never heard of myrrh before,
   I don't know where it's found.
   I haven't any frankincense,
   There's not much gold around:
   Chorus

3 I have no words of good advice
   To help him on his way,
   But there is one thing I can do
   Upon this special day:
   Chorus

Words: Elizabeth Bennett   Music: Colin Evans

118

Candle in the window

1 When the win-ter day is dy-ing And the wind is blow-ing wild, Lis-ten

for a lone-ly cry-ing. It may be a wan-d'ring child. *Light a*

can-dle in your win-dow Let the night know that you care, Light a

can-dle in the win-dow, It may guide the Christ-Child there.

2 When at times you fear to follow
On the track that you must tread,
Friendly promises are hollow
For the tests that lie ahead —
Light a candle in your window
When your final hope is gone.
Light a candle in the window,
And the Child will lead you on.

3 When the world outside is waiting
But you can't give any more —
There's no end to war and hating
And you long to close the door —
Light a candle in your window
Let it shine beyond your pain.
Light a candle in the window,
And the Child will come again.

Words: Arthur Scholey   Music: John Jones

119

The holly and the ivy

2 The holly bears a blossom,
As white as the lily flower;
And Mary bore sweet Jesus Christ,
To be our sweet Saviour:
Chorus

3 The holly bears a berry,
As red as any blood;
And Mary bore sweet Jesus Christ
To do poor sinners good.
Chorus

4 The holly bears a prickle,
As sharp as any thorn,
And Mary bore sweet Jesus Christ
On Christmas Day in the morn:
Chorus

5 The holly bears a bark,
As bitter as any gall;
And Mary bore sweet Jesus Christ
For to redeem us all:
Chorus

6 The holly and the ivy,
When they are both full grown,
Of all the trees that are in the wood,
The holly bears the crown:
Chorus

Words: Traditional Music: John Gardner

*This is an adaptation of John Gardner's original
arrangement which is printed in full as the next item overleaf.*

120 As I went riding by

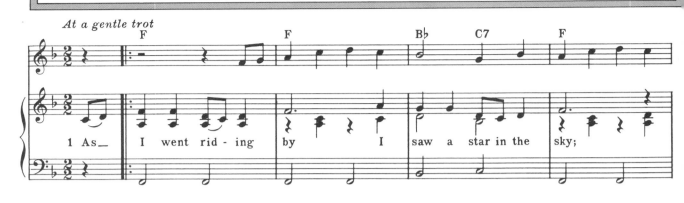

At a gentle trot

1 As— I went rid-ing by I saw a star in the sky;

I fol-lowed where it led— And found a man-ger bed: *Lit-tle*

Je - sus show me the way of your love, Lit-tle Je - sus show me the way of your

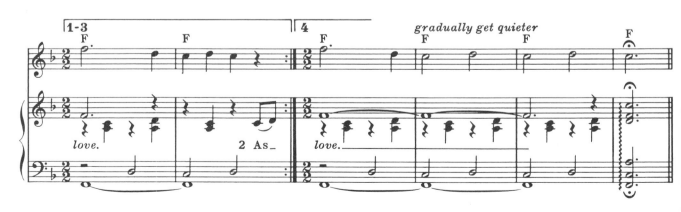

love. 2 As— love.

2 As I stood quietly still,
   Some shepherds came from the hill;
   Their eyes were bright with joy —
   To find the baby boy:
   Chorus

3 As I went riding back,
   Some camels passed on the track;
   Three kings had seen the star —
   And hurried from afar:
   Chorus

4 As I rode home to bed,
   A thought came into my head:
   God must love ev'ryone —
   To give the world his son:
   Chorus

Words: Cecily Taylor   Music: Richard Graves

121

The Virgin Mary

With a swing

1 The Vir-gin Ma-ry had a ba-by boy,__ The Vir-gin Ma-ry had a ba-by boy,__ The Vir-gin Ma-ry had a ba-by boy,__ And they say that his name was Je-sus.__

Chorus

He came from the glo-ry, He came from the glo-ri-ous king-dom.

Oh yes, be-liev-er! Oh yes, be-liev-er!

He came__from the glo-ry, He came from the glo-ri-ous king-dom.

2 The angels sang when the baby was born,
  The angels sang when the baby was born,
  The angels sang when the baby was born,
  And they say that his name was Jesus.
  Chorus

3 The shepherds ran to see the baby boy,
  The shepherds ran to see the baby boy,
  The shepherds ran to see the baby boy,
  And they say that his name was Jesus.
  Chorus

4 The wise men wondered where the baby was born,
  The wise men wondered where the baby was born,
  The wise men wondered where the baby was born,
  And they say that his name was Jesus.
  Chorus

Traditional

122

Christmas, Christmas

With a steady rhythm

1 Christ - mas, Christ - mas, ce - le - brate the time of__ year,

Spe - cial days__ and spe - cial cus - toms, Spe - cial foods and spe - cial gifts,

Raise your voi - ces in a greet - ing, Hap - py fes - ti - val, that's our__ wish.

Words: Geoffrey Gardner   Music: Traditional
This can be used for most popular festivals: Easter, Diwali, Navratri, Holi, Hannukah, Sukkot, Passover, Eid, Baisakhi, etc. Substitute the name of the appropriate festival. The song can be sung several times, possibly becoming faster each time.

123

Mary had a baby

With a joyful rhythm

1 Ma-ry had a ba-by, Yes, Lord; Ma-ry had a ba-by, Yes, my Lord; Ma-ry had a ba-by, Yes, Lord; The peo-ple came to wor-ship him in Beth-le-hem.

2 What did she name him? Yes, Lord . . .

3 She called him Jesus, yes, Lord . . .

4 Where was he born? Yes, Lord . . .

5 Born in a stable, Yes, Lord . . .

6 Where did they lay him? Yes, Lord . . .

7 Laid him in a manger, yes, Lord . . .

Traditional

124 Riding out

Lightly—in the '20's style

1. Rid-ing out a-cross the de - sert, Trav-'lling o-ver sand-y
   Leav-ing all their friends be - hind them, Guid-ed by the star so

plains, Comes a com-pa-ny of wise men, Mov-ing stea-di-ly a-long their
bright, Now they've got to keep on go - ing, Must not let the star get out of

1. way;
2. sight.

Chorus

Rid-ing through the de - sert,

Gen-tly the wise men go, On-wards to the king who was

pro-mised long a - go; But they don't know where they're going to

find___ him There's ma - ny towns to search So they'll keep on

Fol - low-ing the star, For it will lead them to his place of birth.

2 Wise men on their desert journey,
  Travelled many miles so far,
  Though they're getting tired and weary,
  Town of Bethlehem is not too far:
  How they long to worship Jesus
  And honour him with royal gifts,
  Hearts are full of joy and wonder,
  As they're searching for the new born king.
  Chorus

Words and music: Peter Ratcliffe

125

Standing in the rain

Chorus
With movement

Stand-ing in the rain, Knock-ing on the win-dow, Knock-ing on the win-dow On a Christ-mas Day. There he is a-gain, Knock-ing on the win-dow, Knock-ing on the win-dow In the same old way.

Fine

Verse

1 No use knock-ing on the win-dow. There is no-thing we can do, sir. All the

Chorus

2 No, we haven't got a manger,
   No, we haven't got a stable;
   Till you woke us with your knocking,
   We were sleeping like the dead, sir!
   Chorus

Words and music: Sydney Carter

126

Little star

Chorus
Smooth and flowing

Lit-tle star stay with us, Light-en the dark-ness Shine through this long night And show us the way. 1 Lit-tle star shin-ing, To-night we are feel-ing You lead-ing us home Though the jour-ney is long. All down the cen-tur-ies Trav'llers have seen you, And wel-comed the warmth Of your si-lent night song.

D.C. al Fine

Chorus

2 Once you gave light
   To a dimly lit stable,
   And melted the chill,
   Where the new baby lay;

Silently, gently,
His sleeping you guarded,
And stayed till the dawn
Of another new day.
Chorus

Words and music: Jancis Harvey

127

Christmas time

Joyfully

1 Christ-mas time is here, Come and ce - le - brate, Come and ce - le-brate, Come and ce - le-brate, Christ-mas time is here, Come and ce - le-brate, Lift your voice in song.

2 Decorate your rooms,
Come and celebrate . . .

3 Gather with your friends,
Come and celebrate . . .

4 Meet to worship God,
Come and celebrate . . .

5 Hear the tales of old,
Come and celebrate . . .

6 Share the special food,
Come and celebrate . . .

7 See the lighted lamps,
Come and celeberate . . .

Words: Geoffrey Gardner
Music: Traditional

'Christmas time is here', could be replaced by the names of other festivals:

Judaism
Pesach time is here (*Passover*)
Rosh Hashanah's here (*The New Year*)
Purim time is here
Sukkot time is here
Hannukah is here

Sikhism
Baisakhi is here
The Guru's day is here (*for Guru Nanak's Birthday*)

Christianity
Advent time is here
Easter time is here
Whitsun time is here
Pentecost is here
Harvest time is here

Hinduism
Diwali is here
Navratri is here
Holi time is here

Islam
Eid ul Fitr's here
The Prophet's day is here
(*for the Birthday of the Prophet*).

Trotting, trotting

2 Many people in Jerusalem
   Thought he should have come on a mighty horse,
   Lead his nation into battle —
   'Happy is he that comes in the name of the Lord!'

3 Many people in Jerusalem
   Were amazed to see such a quiet man
   Trotting, trotting on a donkey,
   'Happy is he that comes in the name of the Lord!'

4 Trotting, trotting through Jerusalem,
   Jesus sitting on a donkey's back,
   Let us all join in the singing,
   'Happy is he that comes in the name of the Lord!'

Words and music: Eric Reid

Jesus in the garden

1 Je-sus in the gar-den, Sad and left a-lone, Sol-diers come to take_ him; His friends have run for home. Je-sus in the court-room, Sad and left a-lone, Peo-ple come to mock him In robe and crown of thorns.

2 Je-sus on the hill-side, Sad and left a-lone, In the si-lent dark-ness He dies there on his own. Hid-ing in their home. Dis-ci-ples lock the door, Fright-ened of the peo-ple; They go out-side no more.

3 Dis-ci-ples in the room Feel sad-ness turn to joy, Know there's work for them to do,_ Throw o-pen wide the door.

Words: John Tearnan   Music: Douglas Coombes

130

All in an Easter garden

Smoothly

1 All in an Easter Garden, Before the break of day, An angel came for Je - sus, And rolled the stone a - way. And when his friends came seek-ing, With myrrh and spi - ces rare, They found the an - gels at the door, But Je - sus was not there.

2 All in an Easter garden,
   Where water lilies bloom,
   The angels gave their message,
   Beside an empty tomb;
   'He is not here, but come and see
   The place where Jesus lay:
   The Lord of life is risen indeed,
   For this is Easter Day.'

Traditional

131
Now the green blade rises

Lightly, but not too quickly

1 Now the green blade ri - ses from the_ bur-ied grain, Wheat that in the dark earth ma - ny_ days has lain: Love lives a - gain, that with the dead has been: Love is come a - gain like wheat that's spring-ing green.

2 In the grave they laid him, love whom men had slain,
Thinking that never he would wake again:
Laid in the earth like grain that sleeps unseen:
Love is come again like wheat that's springing green.

3 Forth he came at Easter, like the risen grain,
He that for three days in the grave had lain:
Live from the dead my risen Lord is seen:
Love is come again like wheat that's springing green.

4 When our hearts are wintry, grieving or in pain,
Your touch can call us back to life again:
Fields of our heart that dead and bare have been:
Love is come again like wheat that's springing green.

Words: J. M. C. Crum (adapted by Geoffrey Gardner)   Music: Traditional French Carol

132

When from the sky

With a gentle lilt

1 When from the sky in the splen-dour of sum-mer Sun-light pours down o-ver roof, o-ver wood, We sing of the kind-ness, ex-tra-va-gant kind-ness, Of God who is Fa-ther and Lord of all good.

2 When all around us the glory of autumn
Colours the gardens, the fields and the hills,
We sing of the wonder, unspeakable wonder,
Of God who with joy both begins and fulfils.

3 When in the coldness and deadness of winter
Storms from the east with their bluster begin,
We sing of that morning, mysterious morning,
When Jesus was born in the barn of an inn.

4 When in the gladness and greenness of springtime
Winter is over in life and in light,
We sing of that Easter, miraculous Easter,
That shattered the darkness and dread of the night.

Words: Alan T. Dale   Music: Traditional, based on an Irish melody

133
Lord of the harvest

Chorus
With an easy swing

Lord of the har - vest, Lord of the field, Give thanks now to God in na - ture re - vealed.

Verse

1 Give thanks for the sun, the wind and the rain And thanks for the crops that feed us a - gain. The corn safe - ly cut is gath-ered in - side We thank you, oh Lord, that you can pro - vide.

Chorus

2 The trees ripe with fruit stand proud in the sun,
We gather them now that summer is gone.
For yours is the wonder, yours is the power,
Yours is the glory of fruit and of flower.
Chorus

3 So in all our plenty, help us to see,
The needs all around whatever they be.
With food for the body, strength for the soul,
It's healing and caring, making them whole.
Chorus

Words and music: Jancis Harvey

134
I planted a seed

With movement

1 I plant - ed a seed And now that seed is grow - ing, Oh,

how that seed is grow - ing Out of all the ground of me! I plant - ed a seed But

there's no way of know - ing, But there's no way of know - ing Is it fruit or flow'r or weed? There

is no way of show - ing Till it blooms for all to see.

2 I planted a thought
   And now that thought is taking,
   Oh, how that thought is taking
   Over all the mind of me!
   I planted a thought,
   And, love or hate, it's breaking,
   And, love or hate, it's breaking
   Out and never will be caught;
   And love or hate it's making
   Of the way you think of me.

3 I planted a word
   And now that word is yelling,
   Oh, how that word is yelling
   Out of all the mouth of me!
   I planted a word
   And truth or lie it's telling,
   And truth or lie it's telling
   Just whenever it is heard.
   Whatever it is spelling,
   It will soon be clear to see.

4 I planted a deed
   And now that deed is spreading,
   Oh, how that deed is spreading
   Far beyond the reach of me!
   I planted a deed,
   For good or bad it's heading,
   For good or bad it's heading —
   Oh who knows where it will lead?
   Should I be glad, or dreading —
   Here it comes straight back to me!

Words: Arthur Scholey   Music: John Jones
This is based on the 'Parable of the sower' (Luke 8).

135
Pears and apples

Rhythmically

1 Pears and ap-ples, wheat and grapes Ma - ny tex-tures, ma - ny shapes Fall-ing leaves in gold - en drifts Thank you God, for har - vest gifts.

2 Flashing shoals of silver fish,
Every colour you could wish;
Fishing boats, for you and me
Reap the harvest of the sea.

3 Deep beneath the ocean floor
Fuel and power have lain in store,
Brought to us through dangerous toil
Thank you, God, for gas and oil.

4 Coal black diamonds in the earth,
Ancient forests gave them birth;
Skill and labour now combine
Reaping harvests of the mine.

5 Earth and ocean, plant and beast,
Altogether make the feast;
All who long to share your grace
At your table have their place.

6 Loving Lord, we know you care;
May we all your goodness share;
Save us from all selfish greed,
Finding you in those in need.

Words: Paul Booth   Music: Douglas Coombes

136

We thank you Lord

Moderate tempo

1 We thank you Lord for_ all_ we_ eat, From far-mers' fields and o - ceans deep, We thank you_ too for those who_ toil The_ long_ year round on sea and soil.

2 In stormy seas and shrieking gales,
In snow and ice and thunderous hail,
Men plough the waves and sow their nets;
They reap their harvest cold and wet.

3 From break of day till darkness falls,
In summer sun and winter squalls,
Our land is worked and tilled and sown,
'Till all hands ache and all backs groan.

4 We thank you too for those who drive
To bring our food where we can buy.
In shops and stores and market square,
So many work to help us there.

5 For those who live in distant lands
And work so hard in dust and sand;
Dear Lord, we pray that they will too
Have food enough to eat and grow.

Words and music: Robert Smith

137
Michaelmas daisies

With bounce

1 Mich-ael-mas dai-ses pur - ple in the bor-der, Big fat leeks all stand-ing up in or-der,

Whis-kered bar-ley talk - ing to the breeze, Low hung boughs of la - den ap-ple trees,

Chug-ging en-gines rea - dy for the reap-ing, Pounds of chut-ney la - belled for the keep-ing,

Gi - ant mar-rows win - ning ev-'ry prize, Bub-bling jars of el - der-ber-ry wine; It's

har - vest time, har-vest time a - gain, Har - vest

2 Stocky-built trawlers landing with their catches,
Berries gathered, never mind the scratches,
Warm and hazy Indian summer days,
Swallows leaving for another place,
Fruits are bottled, others in the deep freeze,
Silken poppies blushing in the corn-fields,
'Don't bring muddy boots into the hall!',
Golden onions hanging on a wall;
It's harvest time, harvest time again,
Harvest time, thanks to sun and rain,
A time to take and a time to give,
A time to say that it's a joy to live
At harvest time.
Mellow, fruitful harvest time.

Words and music: Estelle White

138
Now we sing

Firmly and steadily

1 Now we sing a har-vest song, Clear and joy - ful, loud and strong;

Think of bread and think of meat, Think of all we have to eat;

All God's gifts to us in love, Earth and rain and sun a - bove,

Thank you, God, for all you give, Thank you, God, by whom we live.

2 Now we sing a sadder song,
　Of injustice, hunger, wrong,
　Those with not enough to eat,
　Suffering every sort of need.
　They've no home, no work, no pay.
　Scraping through from day to day.
　Do they thank you that they live?
　Thank you, God, that we can give.

3 As we sing our harvest song,
　Clear and joyful, loud and strong,
　Help us, Father, now to see.
　How to set those people free;
　How to share the gifts you give
　So that they may also live,
　So the harvest song may sound
　To your praise the earth around.

Words: Alex Mitchell   Music: G. J. Elvey

139
The sharing bread

Expressively

1 Now the har-vest is all ga-thered, Let us eat the Shar-ing Bread, In our fam'ly all to-ge-ther, As our cus-tom is, we said. And we pass the Bread a-mong us, Thank-ing God that all are fed.

2 But there comes a gentle knocking,
Just before we break the Bread,
From our neighbours in the doorway:
'Harvest failed for us,' they said.
So we share the Bread among them,
Thanking God that all are fed.

3 Soon we hear a growing murmur,
As we eat the Sharing Bread,
From the neighbours of our neighbours:
'We are starving, friends,' it said.
Then we stretch the Bread out further
Thanking God that all are fed.

4 When the world begins to clamour,
We cry, 'Take our Sharing Bread,
Miracles we cannot offer!'
'Oh, it happened once,' they said,
'Thousands of us ate together
Thanking God that all are fed.'

Words: Arthur Scholey   Music: Douglas Coombes

140

The Peace prayer

(Two-part version)

(1) Lead me from death to life,
(2) *Lead me from death to life,*
(1) From falsehood to truth,
(2) *From falsehood to truth.*

(1) Lead me from despair to hope,
(2) *Lead me from despair to hope,*
(1) From fear to trust,
(2) *From fear to trust.*

(1) Lead me from hate to love,
(2) *Lead me from hate to love,*
(1) From war to peace,
(2) *From war to peace.*

(1) Let peace fill our heart, our world,
(2) *Let peace fill our heart, our world,*
(1) Our universe
(2) *Our universe.*

See the next page for the Short version.

Words adapted by Satish Kumar from 'The Upanishads'. Music by Donald Swann. In 1981 Mother Teresa urged everyone to use The Peace Prayer daily. The song can be sung by two groups, indicated by (1) and (2). Group (2) echoes the tune and words sung by Group (1). Alternatively, it can be sung without the echoing lines.

Short version
Lead me from death to life,
From falsehood to truth.

Lead me from despair to hope,
From fear to trust.

Lead me from hate to love,
From war to peace.

Let peace fill our heart, our world,
Our universe.

Words: Adapted from 'The Upanishads' by Satish Kumar   Music: Donald Swann

Shalom

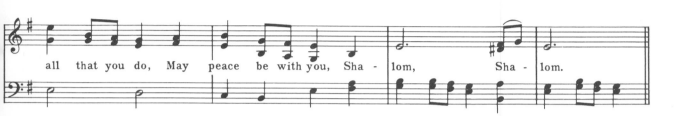

Steadily and smoothly

Sha - lom, Sha - lom, May peace be with you, Through-out your days; In

all that you do, May peace be with you, Sha - lom, Sha - lom.

Words: Traditional, adapted by Geoffrey Gardner   Music: Traditional
'Shalom' is a Hebrew word meaning 'peace'. This song may be sung as a round.

130

142

Down by the riverside

stu-dy war no more, I ain't gon-na stu-dy _____ war no more. _____

2 I'm gonna talk with the Prince of peace,
   Down by the riverside,
   Down by the riverside,
   Down by the riverside,
   I'm gonna talk with the Prince of peace,
   Down by the riverside,
   Down by the riverside.
   Chorus

3 I'm gonna shake hands with everyone,
   Down by the riverside,
   Down by the riverside,
   Down by the riverside,
   I'm gonna shake hands with every one,
   Down by the riverside,
   Down by the riverside.
   Chorus

4 I'm gonna walk with my friends in peace,
   Down by the riverside,
   Down by the riverside,
   Down by the riverside,
   I'm gonna walk with my friends in peace,
   Down by the riverside,
   Down by the riverside.
   Chorus

Traditional

143

I've got peace like a river

2 I've got love like a river,
   Love like a river,
   I've got love like a river in my soul;
   I've got love like a river,
   Love like a river,
   I've got love like a river in my soul.

3 I've got joy like a river,
   Joy like a river,
   I've got joy like a river in my soul;
   I've got joy like a river,
   Joy like a river,
   I've got joy like a river in my soul.

4 I've got hope like a river,
   Hope like a river,
   I've got hope like a river in my soul;
   I've got hope like a river,
   Hope like a river,
   I've got hope like a river in my soul.

Words: Traditional   Music: John Jones

Peace is flowing

Quick, flowing tempo

1 Peace is flow-ing like a ri - ver, Flow - ing out through you and me, ___

Spread - ing out in -to the de - sert, Set - ting all the peo-ple free.

2 Love is flowing like a river,
   Flowing out through you and me,
   Spreading out into the desert,
   Setting all the people free.

3 Joy is flowing like a river,
   Flowing out through you and me,
   Spreading out into the desert,
   Setting all the people free.

4 Hope is flowing like a river,
   Flowing out through you and me,
   Spreading out into the desert,
   Setting all the people free.

Words and music: Traditional

145

The pollen of peace

Chorus

2 All it needs is our love to make it grow;
  All it needs is our hopefulness to show;
  And tell those who are choked with fear
  That the Prince of peace is here;
  All it needs is our love to make it grow.
  Chorus

*This was written by Roger Courtney for the Corrymeela Community,
which works to bring peace and reconciliation in Northern Ireland.*

146

The pilgrims' hymn

1 We ask that we live and we la-bour in peace, in peace, Each one shall be our neigh-bour in peace, in peace. Dis-trust and ha-tred will turn to love, All the pris-'ners freed, And our on-ly war will be the one A-gainst all hu-man need.

2 We work for the end of disunion in truth, in truth;
  That all may be one communion in truth, in truth;
  We choose the road of peace and prayer
  Countless pilgrims trod,
  So that Hindu, Muslim, Christian, Jew,
  We all can worship one God.

3 We call to our friends and our brothers, unite, unite!
  That all may live for others, unite, unite!
  And so the nations will be as one,
  One the flag unfurled,
  One law, one faith, one hope, one truth,
  One people and one world.

Words and music: Donald Swann

147

The prayer of St Francis

Prayerfully

1 Make me a chan-nel of your peace. _____ Where there is ha-tred,

let me bring your love; _____ Where there is in-ju-ry, your par-don,

Lord; _____ And where there's doubt, true faith in you. _____ Fine

Chorus

O Mas-ter, grant that I may ne-ver seek _____ So much to be con-

soled as to con-sole, _____ To be un-der-stood as to un-der-

2 Make me a channel of your peace.
  Where there's despair in life, let me bring hope;
  Where there is darkness, only light;
  And where there's sadness, ever joy:
  Chorus

3 Make me a channel of your peace.
  It is in pardoning that we are pardoned,
  In giving to all men that we receive,
  And in dying that we're born to eternal life.

Words and music: Sebastian Temple
This is based on 'The prayer of St Francis'.

148

Let the world rejoice together

Strongly–start steadily and gradually get faster

Let the world re-joice to-ge-ther al-le-lu – ia, East and West with North and South sing al-le-lu – ia. al-le-lu – ia. Lift your voi – ces, all you peo-ple, Share with o – thers what you can, Bring-ing__ care to those who need it, Peace in ev – 'ry__ land, Peace in ev – 'ry__ land.

*If sung through twice, get faster during the second time.

Words: Geoffrey Gardner   Music: Traditional
The verse is repeated, getting faster each time.

149

The vine and the fig tree

Traditional
This is based on words from Micah 4:3. This song may be sung as a round.

INDEX: Page numbers (feint) and song numbers (**bold**).
Titles which are different from the first line appear in italics.

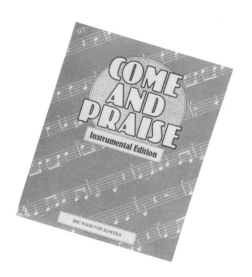

Over two million copies of this BBC hymn book have been sold to schools and churches. It contains 72 contemporary and traditional songs. There are 3 book editions still available.

The words edition

There are sections on the created world, the life of Jesus, thanksgiving, the journey of life, daily life and the human family.

The piano edition

This contains, with the words, a simplified piano accompaniment, a part for melodic instruments such as recorders, and guitar chords.

The instrumental edition

For each hymn four parts are printed to allow for a range of instrumental accompaniments: the melody, two melodic parts, a bass part. There are also guitar chords and percussion parts.

For details, please contact BBC School Publications, PO Box 234, Wetherby, West Yorkshire, LS23 7EU, telephone number: (0937) 541001.